HOUSE OF BALLOONS

JIYA THAKUR

Made with ♥ on the Notion Press Platform
www.notionpress.com

"If it hurts to breathe, open the window"

Contents

Contents

Contents

Preface

As a debut author, I never intended for this book to be a literary endeavor. It started out as a way of personal exploration, a way to process my thoughts and experiences. However, as I delved deeper into the writing process, I realized that this book could be a medium through which I could use my words to explore complex issues and share my perspective on how life goes around. While some elements of the book are directly inspired by my own life experiences, some other are interwoven with universal themes that resonate with all of us. Through my writing, I hope to show that even the most difficult situations can have a positive side, and that our imperfections are what make us truly human. I am excited to share my book with the world and inspire others to embrace their own distinctive journeys.

Acknowledgements

Thank you, **Mom** for showing blind faith in my abilities and standing by my side throughout the publishing process of the book and supporting me whole-heartedly in all my endeavours, I am really grateful to have you in my life. **Dad**, I am hugely thankful to you for giving me the first push into writing this book and encouraging me all the time. I am lucky to have you both in my life<3. huge thanks to my brother, **Saksham Thakur,** My favorite person and all-time cheerleader, I couldn't have done this without your support, heartening and constant love.

Saksham Tiwari, you deserve a special mention here for being my cover art illustrator, thankyou for patiently supporting me and being there when I desperately needed a helping hand, we gang!!

I am truly grateful to my aunt **Jyoti vij ahuja** for having her writerly touch that brought my book to life :)

1. INTRO

Life is a journey, full of twists and turns,
With highs and lows, and many lessons to learn.
Embrace the journey, with all its bends,
For in it's ups and down, make us who we are in the end.

2. ECHOES OF SILENCE

Right or wrong linger on your brain.
But still, you do it not contemplating about your pain.
All people do is think about themselves.
Shouldn't someone else have a same say as them?
I cut myself up and can't even look at my face.
While he goes around and climbs up that staircase.
He'll always have a place in my heart that's inevitable.
But the impact on my life made this all look so unintelligible.
Each setback pushes me more, will the thoughts in my head rot me to core?
It stinks of hate it stinks of misery it stinks of loneliness but what did I do to deserve this for so long?
Gullibility comes as a new crime I just wanted him to be mine.
The shame the hurt gets me on the dirt can I even subliminally imagine.
Why would this happen something so tragic.
I remind myself of this pretty girl she's so pout but far too hollow.
Am I turning out to be like her?

3. CLASS FIGHT

In a class filled with whispers and stares
She stands alone so bare.
She longs for acceptance, a place in between.
With each passing day she's left on side
As classmates form cliques their bonds fortified
But within her heart a flame still burns bright
A spirit resilient ready to take on a flight.
She knows her worth, her potential untold.
In her uniqueness a story unfolds
For exclusion may sting but it cannot define
A girl who is destined to shine.
In her journey she will surely find her way
Proving that exclusion cannot drive you astray.

4. Deserted

It was the middle of class and the teacher wasn't looking

5. LIFE OF THE PARTY

Behind the painted walls, a tale unfolds.
Of a love so twisted where virulence takes hold
A heart once pure, now tainted with disdain.
A new lover emerges causing pain.
At first, she gives a spark, an enchanting allure.
But beneath the cover a darkness obscure
She thrives on control,
A puppeteer's delight, pulling strings.
Causing chaos day and night
The love is a poison.
Slowly seeping in
Leaving other broken, lost within
Because once she also felt the same
Yet she became so inhumane.
She feeds on insecurity, leaving her partner drowning in tears.
For the one caught in such embrace
It's crucial to find oneself and leave that space.
Recollect soul, you deserve better.
A love should uplift, not fetter.

You've been thinking about being bad, ever since I put you on

6. MRS. POTATO HEAD

Is it true that pain is beauty?
Does a new face come with a warranty?
Will a pretty face make it better?
Thousands of questions linger on her head.
In the shadows of doubt, insecurity creeps
A silent thief that steals her peace
In the mirror she sees a reflection
Which is just clouded by judgement and her own perception.
Society's standards, they weigh her down,
Striving for perfection, wearing a frown.
Whispering lies, planting seeds of fear,
Which makes us lose our own self, oh so dear.
Comparing ourselves to an unattainable ideal,
We forget our own worth, our own appeal.
Plastic Plastic Plastic, she has lost it now.
Will someone still be able to save her somehow?

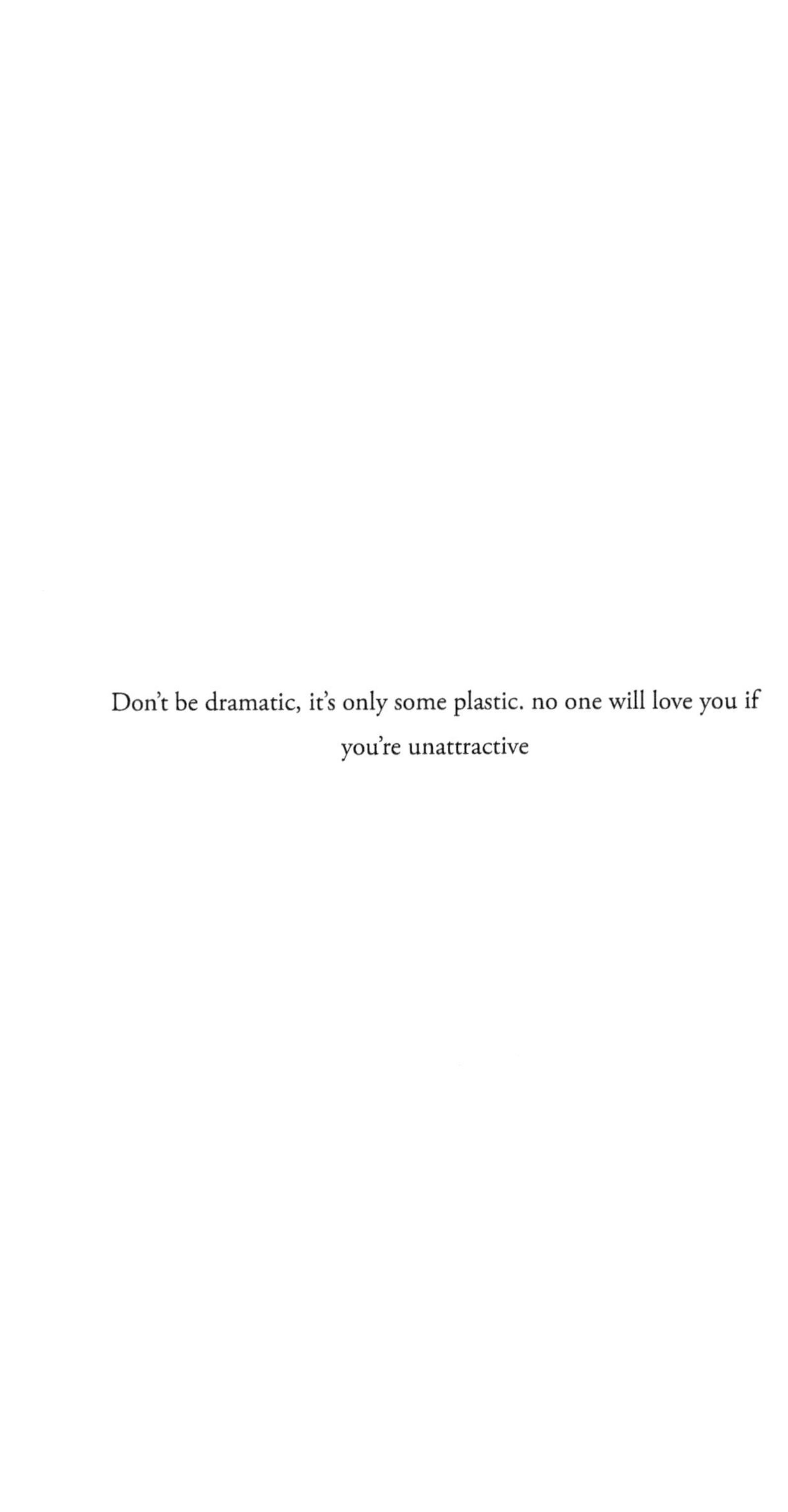

Don’t be dramatic, it’s only some plastic. no one will love you if you’re unattractive

7. CRAB'S RACE

It's a crabs race everywhere so far and so awry.
Where everyone raises their shell so bright,
The crabs scuttle readily for another fight.
Some crabs stumble, lose their way.
But they rise again ready to play.
The head of crustacean family gives a command.
To the new and old members of the clan and the whole band
The finish line beckons, a shimmering prize,
But the cost of this competition, hidden in disguise.
Oh, what a sight, this crab's race so grim,
A mirror reflecting the worst of human whim.
Where kindness and empathy are cast aside,
In the relentless pursuit of selfish pride.
So let us pause and reflect on this crabby display,
And remember the lessons learned on this fateful day.

8. Metaphor or reality?

Crab mentality is a phenomenon where people react negatively, in terms of their thoughts, statements, or actions, to those who get ahead of them. The crabs can easily escape from the bucket, but instead, they grab and pull down each other in a selfish competitive manner which prevents any of them to escape, resulting to their collective demise.

9. WICKED GAMES

In shadows deep, In the guise of passion,
Cloaked in charm, with eyes that gleam,
He preys on love like a twisted dream.
With honeyed words and a silken touch,
The exploiter came, taking far too much.
He whispers sweet nothings,
it's a siren's call,
He planted seeds of dread and fear,
Watered with tears, year after year.
The lover gave, the taker took,
In this unbalanced ledger book.
From far a voice called, Beware the predator in love's clothing,
For his affection is nothing but loathing.
But for the blind girl, all alone in this world of masks and masquerade,
She was captivated by his artful play,
Unaware of the price she would pay.
He spun a web of illusion and charm,
Leading her on with his gentle arm.
His promises were like stars above,
But his heart was a cage, devoid of love.
She danced in his shadow, lost in his gaze,

Ignoring the warning signs, the hidden maze.
The maiden fair soon realised, True affection seeks to share,
In a bond that's just, and genuinely fair.

Cloaked

I never dreamed that I'd meet somebody like you

10. CRY TO SLEEP

Tears falling silently in the dead of night
I contemplate if what i did was right,
It grips my heart so tight
I try to shut the world around
But I don't think the fear inside me can be drowned
I toss and turn unable to find rest
My mind turns into a whirlwind, an utter mess
I cry myself to sleep, hoping tomorrow will bring some relief
Each breath feels like a struggle to take, oh for god's sake
I long for peace, for quiet in my head
But there anxiety whispers lies instead
I hold on to hope a solemn deciet
Wishing and praying, that the next day does not deplete

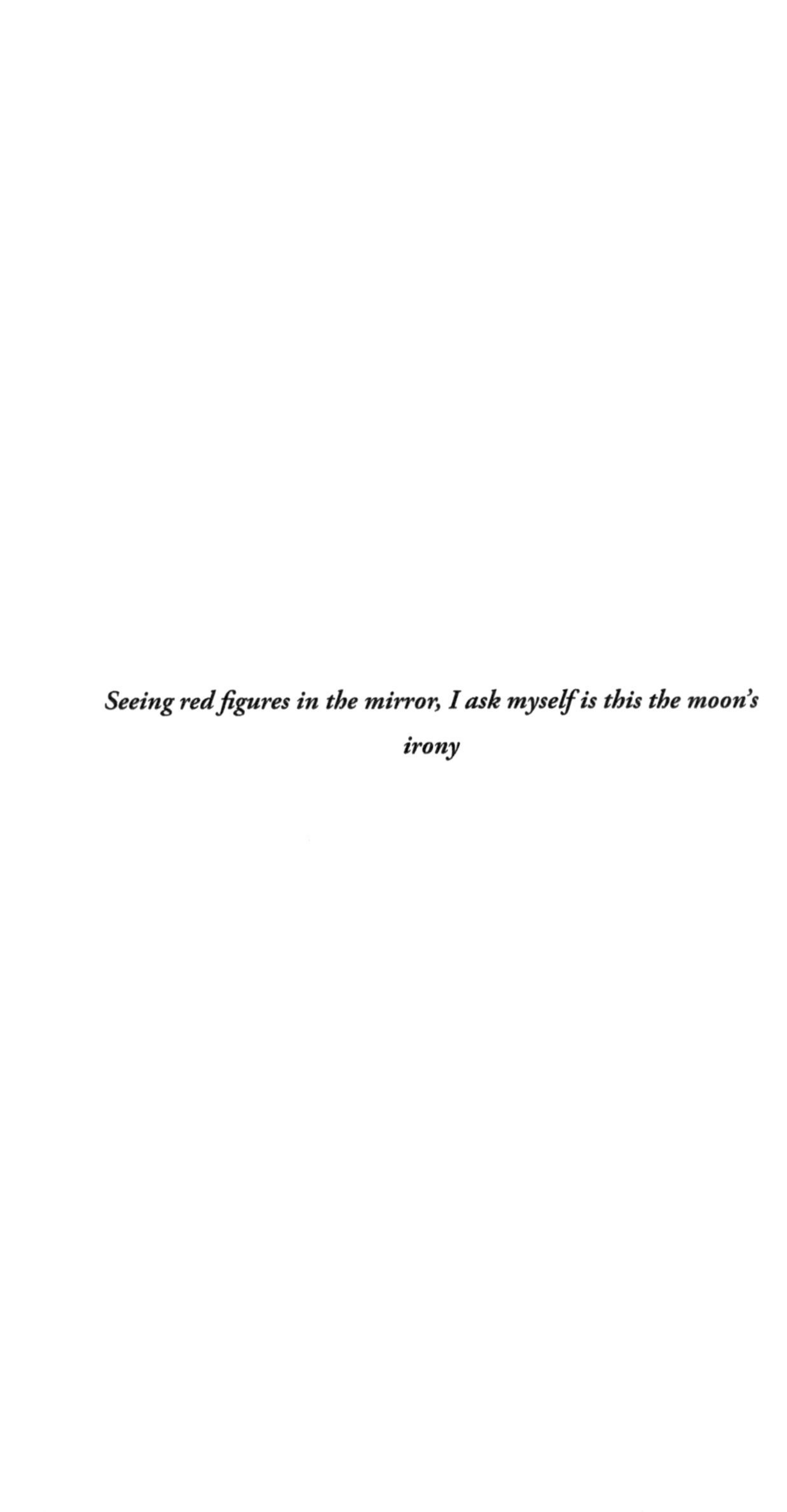

Seeing red figures in the mirror, I ask myself is this the moon's irony

11. TRAINING WHEELS

All these times I'd found myself longing.
For a friend whose heart would burst along with mine in fireworks
Waltzing and rushing towards the same forgotten light,
Leaving the grey madness of the concrete seas behind us,
To sail, fierce and loving, and throw in a big fuss.
Towards lands where madness is that of a different kind.
Dreaming of a lover who'd know every word of my mind.
Each silent secret under my skin
Would open up a whole new world within
I guess I can pull off my training wheels.
Because every time I put my eyes on you,
my heart does nothing but squeals.

12. The love that remembers is my only urge

No training wheels left for you, i'll pull them off for you

13. WHY WOMEN KILL? -1963

Set in the old days of 1963.
Lies a meek housewife, dowdy and frump.
In a quaint little house, she waits alone,
Her husband's whereabouts unknown
She is a faithful wife, devoted and true.
While her spouse's love strays, his loyalty askew.
She tends to the home with care and grace,
While he seeks solace in another's embrace.
Through tear-stained nights and lonely days,
She carries on in a silent haze.
After a point, due to exhaustion and strife
She went up to him holding a kitchen knife.
For I had enough of his antics due to addiction,
That's what I said to the authorities,
When questioned about the scene of the crime,
Reality is it was me who hosted his last drunkard night,
Then pushed him off the rolling edge, as he slipped out his wight.
They won't even suspect me, his poor little wife,
World knows what a good woman I had been,
I killed you my husband for a good cause,

Not seeking for your affection, your biggest weakness
Just a thank you for complying to my last request,

Another
Day in
Paradise!

14. THE HOST

In the shadow cast by the moon's soft glow
A mistress laments, her heart in woe.
Bound by a love so cruel.
She's trapped in a web, a relentless duel.
Her heart once hopeful, now heavy with pain
She dances with a lover that is in vain.
In the secrecy of night, they meet and embrace.
But the price she pays in her own soul's disgrace.
She's the hidden secret the forbidden desire.
Caught in a web of passion and fire.
She's lost in a labyrinth of deceit and lies.
Her spirit withers, her true self slowly dies.
She longs for affection a love that's pure.
Where she can soar, and her soul can endure.
Yet she clings onto the fragments of hope.
In a love twisted where pain and heart elope
For the mistress deserved a love so kind
A love that mends her core leaving no scars behind

There's so much love to pass around so if you wanna go again, you can always call me

15. WHY WOMEN KILL? -1984

Set in late 1984, when fashion was worth more than a dime.
In a mansion full of glitter and gold, lives a lady ever so bold.
With a flair for the extravagant,
She makes sure the couple always looks magnificent.
She sips on champagne, dressed to the nines,
Her elegance and grace simply divine.
Her wardrobe filled with designer labels,
Her parties the talk of the social stables.
The housewife dances in the living room,
Her laughter always filling the gloom.
Behind the walls of luxury and flair
She finds out about her husband's gay affair.
They confront, and yet pretend to be the perfect pair.
Back to the present she thinks to herself,
"Oh, I always knew my husband was never mine"
Our fates were broken but yet again entwined.
A deadly curse came into his way.
He went all shaken and his face turned grey.
Even though he was imperfect but so was I.
I gave him my everything, just to not see him cry.

When the pain became unbearable, he left me with no voice.
He undertook euthanasia and drived a huge mischoice
Nevertheless, I was with him until his last breath.
Dancing tango and celebrating his special death.

I'm a bad walker so can we dance tango?

16. ECSTACY WITHOUT CHEMICALS

Where joy and love intertwine,
Ecstasy without chemicals,
In the beauty of the divine.
A sunset painting the sky,
Or a gentle breeze on your skin,
Natures song plays on
Laughter shared with a friend,
Or a hug that feels like home,
These simple moments of connection,
Where true ecstasy is known.
Embracing our flaws and scars with grace,
We learn to love our unique face.
Ecstasy is not something that needs to be found.
It's the joy within oneself that we need to rebound.
So, let your love of life, reign over the fears of strife.
To the wonders of existence all around
See that's the place true ecstasy is found.

My fickle insecurites, tuning into beauty

17. SPIDER WEB

In the depths of a fragile mind
Lies a war unseen, a torment confined.
Words replace daggers cutting deep within
Mental abuse a silent but haunting sin
Voices of doubt echo through the soul
As the weight of cruel words take on a toll
Every insult, every belittling phrase
Chip away of the spirit
Their hopeful gaze
They twist and turn.
Distorting reality
Leaving the teenager trapped in their mentality.
For it may sear and bruise
It cannot extinguish the fire that ensues.
With support they find their voice
Reclaim their worth making the choice.
Together we can break the chains that bind.
Help them heal and their heart re-aligned.

18. Entanglement

Better off dead than wasting my hours, Flying where I shouldn't be

19. TAG, YOU'RE IT !

In the dead of night, a shadow creeps near,
A sudden silence, a sense of fear.
Into the darkness, a chilling chase.
Bound by chains of false promises and schemes,
Their hopes shattered, lost in darkened dreams.
Bound and gagged, a prisoner of fright,
Lost in a world of endless night.
Like a puppet on strings, they dance to another's tune,
Their autonomy stolen; their spirit marooned.
She remains in this silent prison,
Desperate finding for a way to break free and listen.
Tears fall silently, unheard cries,
As the cruel hands of fate devise.
Alone and helpless, in a stranger's hold,
A nightmare story waiting to unfold.
To the whispers of my heart, the cries of my soul,
Hoping one day I'll find a way to be whole.

20. Coerced

He chased me and he wouldn't stop

21. PARANOID

Do you have dreams?
Are they good or bad?
Do they resemble your future?
Or make you cook up something bad?
Ill tell you how my dreams look like
Oh, they're full of paranoia and disgust.
They make me question who to and who not to trust.
Eyes darting, heart racing,
Minds spinning, thoughts racing.
Is it real or just a trick of the mind?
Seeking solace in the light,
But shadows follow, never out of sight.
I may look like the feeble kind.
But trust me when I say this, I've found what's right.
Just Trust and Remember, in the darkness, you are not alone,
Reach out, seek help, let your fears be known.
That together we stand,
In unity and strength, hand in hand.

22. Void ate me

People think i'm insane because I am frowning all the time, I cannot bear my sorrow, I hate who I was before

23. Lonely star

In the classroom's hush, where knowledge should thrive,
Unfair judgments cut deep, like a sharp knife.
In the shadows of solitude, a lonely soul resides,
Underestimated, overlooked, where their true worth hides.
she just sits their wondering am I really that low? am I really that bad?
while thousands of questions just drive her more mad
Should and shouldn't linger on her head, insecurity just spreads.
Teachers' eyes, clouded by bias and wrong play,
Lead the innocent astray.
The eager hearts and minds, ready to take flight,
But held back by circumstances, out of sight.
Misunderstood and unseen, their voice unheard,
Their potential and talents, like a caged bird.
The gullible one feels the sting of disdain.
Mistaken for weakness, taken for granted,
Their spirit bruised, their trust enchanted.
Through the veil of bias, they strive to break through,
To show the world their strength, their value true.
so, keep believing, in your own worth,
For in the end, you'll prove your strength and mirth.

6+6
3+1
4+5
34+35
6+1

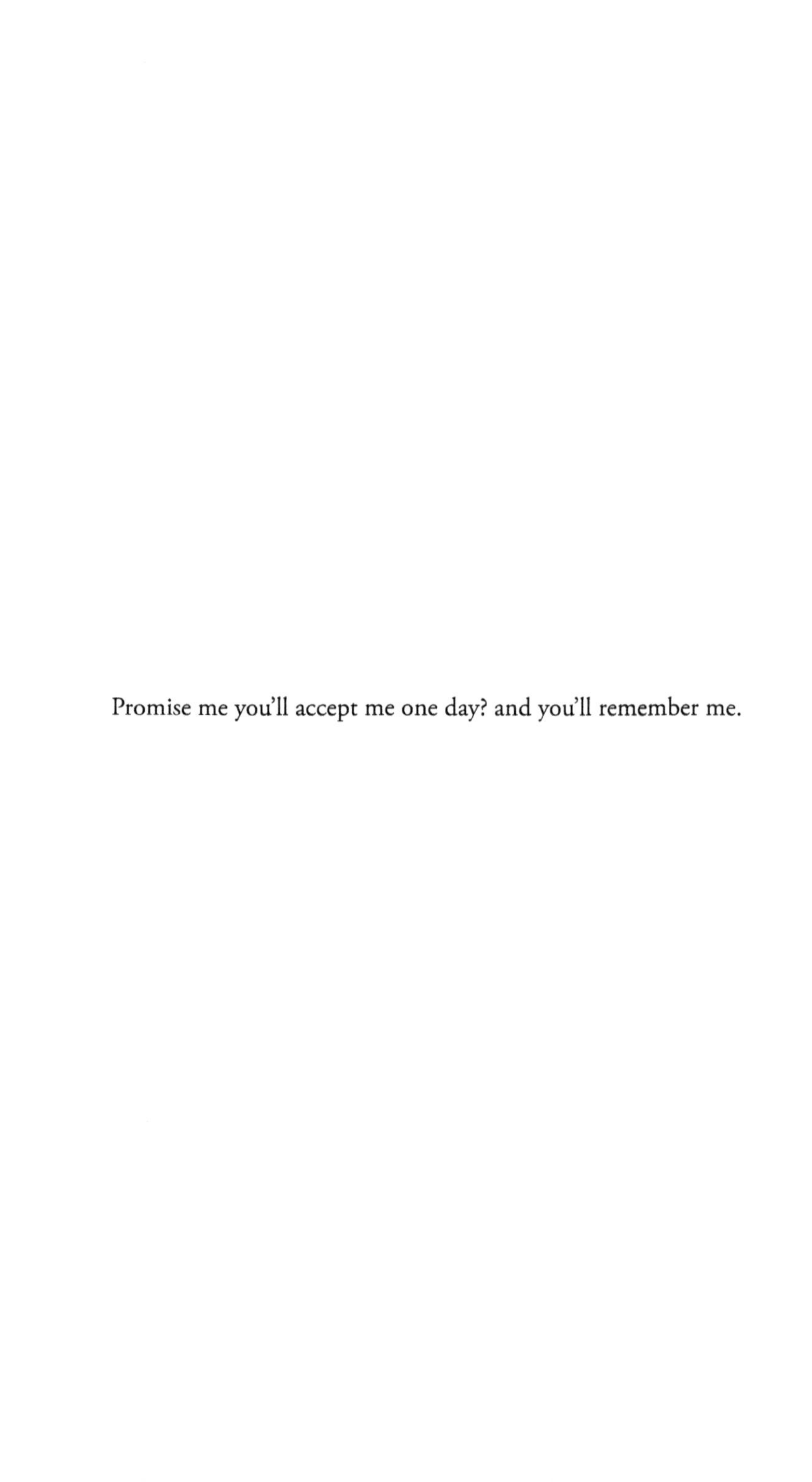

Promise me you'll accept me one day? and you'll remember me.

24. FAERIE SOIREE

She thinks back to herself, When you're not around.
I sink to the ground, how am I supposed to move on?
Her love for him remains steadfast and strong,
Even as she knows she doesn't belong.
Late in the night only a flicker of hope still burns,
For the day when his love finally returns.

Led me astray to the faerie soirée, I know how you make me go crazy every day

25. INITIATION

She stood outside on an unlit, secluded street.
She noticed no screams, no hint of fear.
And saw another man enjoying ruining a creed so clear.
the thought of running must have crossed her mind.
But she went sore to see the man who was twice her size.
It was a stab on the man's pride.
As if the silenced maiden had become a laugh on his manly drive.
So, he seized her pride as she had hurt mine
The cloth was torn in rips of nine.
Rage had clouded all the senses.
When the weapon of obscenity was shoved inside her
Her innocent face was sliced with every jab beside her.
She was hence violated with every sin that night.
Not knowing what was wrong and what was right.
She is shown to cry, bawl and retch.
Trying to cover up her bare body and sewing up the stich.
The taste of her defeat was too hard.
She will now surely burn his heart.
In a guise of a new woman, she penetrated his walls,
Set ablaze the man in one gruesome holocaust.
She chopped the man's head, under the moon in sight.

And left his mangled-up corpse to ignite.
Our sweet dear lady, whom we'll never get to forget.
Tell me, how would she move on and get on with her regret?

Ravishment

All this looks foreign to you

26. LUNCHBOX FRIENDS

Take me home,
i cant bear to stand in the corridor alone anymore
What is it that i do so wrong?
The wall breaks on its own, it isnt so strong
There's a whole world out there
I am just living a play
i try to convince myself, that it's just a shade of blae
With every step, an empty space
No laughter shared, no familiar face,
With past memories, whispers call
Of moments i shared, where now just ghosts sprawl
Thats my bad, that's my bad that i expect it out of them too much
At the end it's only my dreams that crush

Chapter27

We can be friends if you want to be, but only until the clock hits three

Empty halls

I don’t wanna be an actress, living by a script

28. DRAMA CLUB

In the sphere of masks and hidden faces,
In the spotlight of the stage, many people play their part,
Those who fake their care with a deceitful art.
In a drama club where masks are worn,
Their false concern leaves us torn.
words are scripted, their gestures rehearsed,
Their actions speak louder than words,
A facade of perfection, like delicate birds
Behind the scenes, their true colours show,
Their insincerity beginning to glow.
They act as friends, with smiles so bright,
But their intentions hidden from plain sight.
Dancing with ghosts so far and astray,
But when the mask begins to slip,
The truth emerges, from their grip.
Tread carefully in this dramatic scene,
And discern the true from the unseen.

Spectre

I hear my mind speak, they're all just ghosts

29. VALERIE

A heart beats softly reminiscing the dead of time
I long to be true, to honour the bond we share,
But my restless soul wanders, seeking elsewhere.
Through the haze of smoke and neon lights,
Valerie shines like a star in the darkest nights.
The quest for love, is a twisted game,
Leaving hearts in endless shame.
Yearning for a touch, a tender embrace,
I am torn between two worlds, unable to choose,
Caught in a web of lies, unable to refuse.
In the shadows of a broken trust, lies a heart in rust.
I wish I could change, to be the partner you deserve,
But the truth is, my heart is fickle, and it swerves.
I am flawed, imperfect, unable to remain true,
And for that, my love, I am sorry to you.

I know you can see through me so let us sail through

30. HEAVEN OR LAS VEGAS

In the quiet moments, when all is still, I feel this persistent chill.
A gloom that lingers, a weight on my chest,
A feeling of unease, put to the test.
Morals and immorals, a constant fight,
Tearing at the fabric of day and night.
Heaven or Las Vegas, a place in between.
The path is murky, the choices unclear,
As the person grapples with doubt and fear.
In the midst of the highway, a decision must be made,
Heaven or Las Vegas, where fantasies collide,
A paradise of pleasure, where tickers open wide.
The red lights flicker, a seductive glow,
Leading us off the rail, where darkness may grow.
Between the lanes of vice and virtue we tread,
Seeking the balance, where our souls are fed.
So let the battle rage on, let the struggle be real,
For in the conflict, true character reveals.
And in the end, when the dust settles down,
The person will rise, wearing virtue as a crown.

31. Iniquity/Integrity

32. UNTIL DAWN

In the shadows of defeat, we find our strength,
Through failures, we learn to go to greater lengths.
For in the face of failure, we find resilience and grit,
And from the depths of despair, our new spirit is lit.
Through trials and tribulations, we roam,
Seeking a place to call "our own".

Hue of day

Here comes the sun, i’ve been through the night

33. RECESS

People going to try, to tell you made up lies and break up beautiful skies.
It's easier to live, once we understand these souls.
Some stay for a moment, some make us whole.
There comes a time when we must let go.
To release the ties that no longer flow
Holding on to those who no longer serve
Only brings us pain that we don't deserve.
Happiness blooms like a flower,
In every moment, every hour,
It is eventually only us that needs to empower.
Letting go of our own pernicious self.
Avails in getting rid of woe, off the shelf.
Make spaces for new faces, new stories & new dreams.
God will unfold life in its own mystifying schemes.

Part 26

I was too young to see the truth, about the words my grandma
whispered as she brushed down my hair

Author's Request

If you found this book to be intriguing and feel that the book is deserving to be noticed by other people, you can follow some of the steps below :)

1. Share the book with your friends and ask people you know to buy it.
2. Drop a review on Amazon or Goodreads.
3. Share the book on social media platforms- Instagram, Twitter, etc. Tag me if possible!
4. If any of these tasks are time consuming then just drop me a text and let me know what you think of the book.
5. For any discussions or invite, contact me at "jiya.thakurchat@gmail.com" or "inikoxx5@gmail.com".

About Jiya Thakur

Jiya is a budding author and a humanities student. She is an enthusiastic person who revels to every opportunity to connect with new individuals she meets with in her life, from bustling streets to the tranquil countryside she loves to interact and unravel new perspectives and stories from the people around her. Her passion in arts has always been her constant companion. She's an avid reader and has a keen interest in music which has always held a special place in her heart since her early days. She is also a proficient vocalist who is currently working on the release of her first EP. She is firm in stating her opinions and voicing her thoughts freely as she believes expression is the only way through which we can understand ourselves and better acknowledge the viewpoints of all by our side. She is very straightforward with her thinking and inspired by the transformative power of words. She never imagined herself as an author but the profound shift in her surrounding sparked her newfound interest in writing. She hopes that this book succeeds in resonating and engaging with all the readers!

Reach Out!

You can reach her at:

Email ID- jiya.thakurchat@gmail.com or inikoxx5@gmail.com

Instagram- @jiyathakur_5

www.ingramcontent.com/pod-product-compliance
Lightning Source LLC
LaVergne TN
LVHW021142160826
845679LV00023B/2008